20-10

80-10

Supercool
Subtraction
MAZES

Gabriele Tafuni

90-10

30-10

Capella

This edition published in 2019 by Arcturus Publishing Limited
26/27 Bickels Yard, 151–153 Bermondsey Street,
London SE1 3HA

Copyright © Arcturus Holdings Limited

Illustrated by Gabriele Tafuni
Written by Catherine Casey
Designed by Trudi Webb
Edited by Sebastian Rydberg

ISBN: 978-1-83857-141-2
CH007813NT
Supplier 33, Date 0919 Print run 9218

Printed in China

How to Use This Book

Welcome to the "funtastic" world of supercool subtraction mazes! This activity book is full of exciting scenes to help you learn and become confident with the basics of subtraction.

Locate the start of each maze, and read the instructions to help you solve it.

Some topics come with a Top Tip to help you on the way.

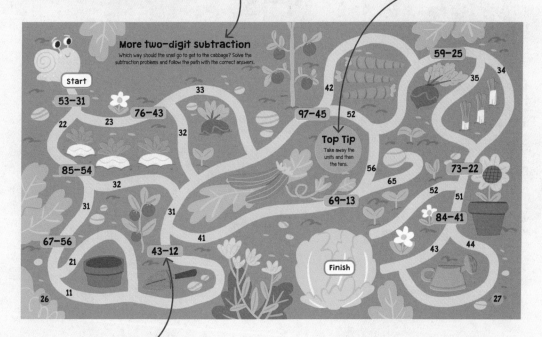

More two-digit subtraction
Which way should the snail go to get to the cabbage? Solve the subtraction problems and follow the path with the correct answers.

start

53−31
76−43
33
59−25
42
97−45   52
35   34
22   23
32

Top Tip
Take away the units and then the tens.

85−54
56
73−22
32
65
52   51
31
69−13
84−41
67−56
31
43−12
41
43   44
21
Finish
26   11
27

Solve each calculation, and then choose the correct path to reach the end.

After you have completed the maze, check that you followed the correct route by turning to pages 30-32.

Number bonds
Number bonds are pairs of numbers that make up a given number. These are some of the number bonds to 10 and 20.

10 Bonds	20 Bonds
1+9	1+19
2+8	2+18
3+7	3+17
4+6	4+16
5+5	5+15

Subtracting single-digit numbers

The princess is hungry, so can you guide her through the castle to the kitchens? Solve the calculations and take the route with the correct answers.

10

5-5

0

9-3

3

6

4

8-5

3

3-1

4

4

7-3

4

Start

10

Top Tip
Count back from the first number to find the correct answer.

8-4

9-7

6-4

6-5

4

5

6

2

2

1

2

2

1

1

5

1

Finish

5

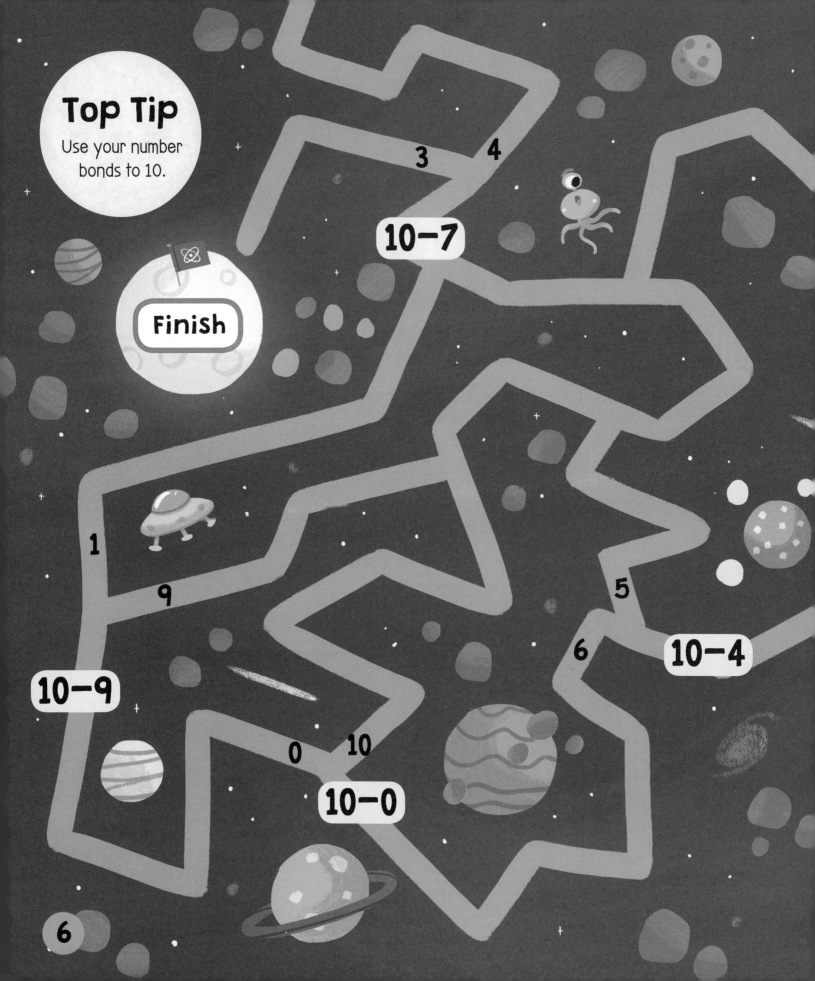

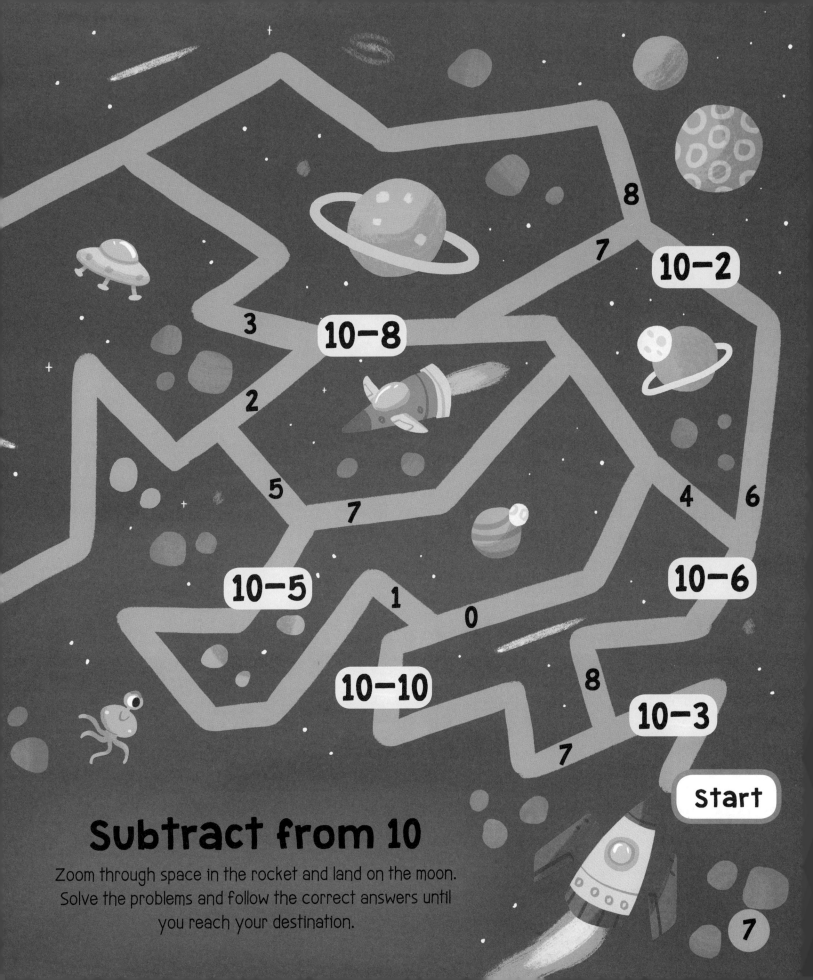

Subtract from 10

Zoom through space in the rocket and land on the moon.
Solve the problems and follow the correct answers until
you reach your destination.

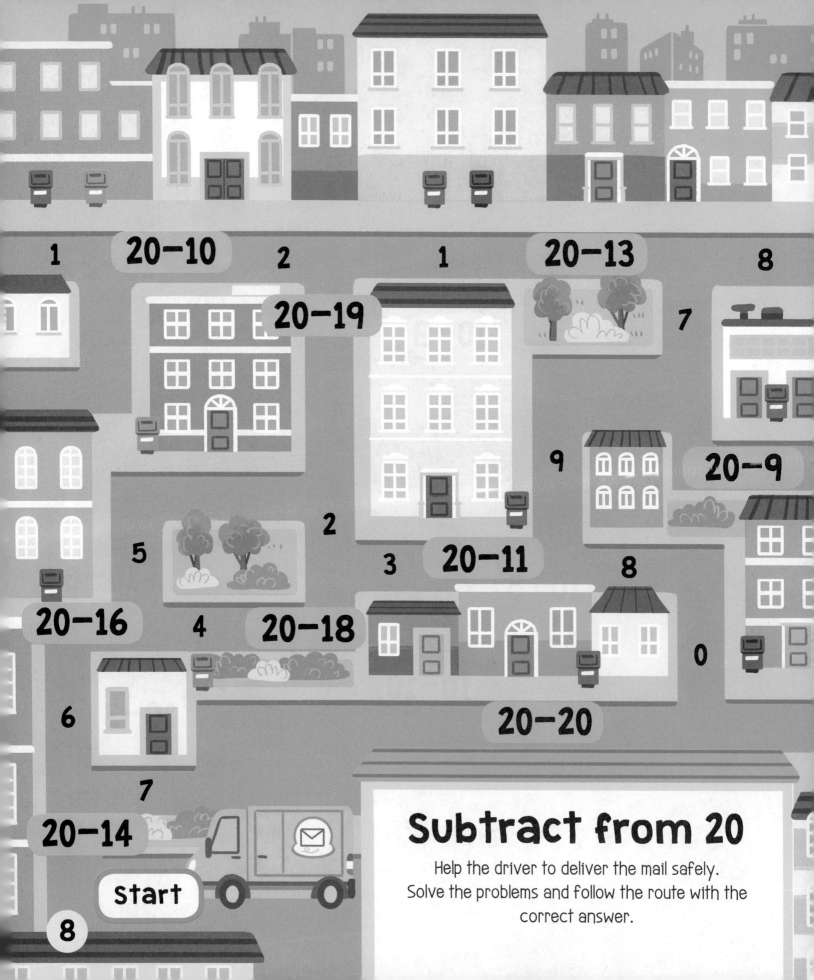

Subtract from 20

Help the driver to deliver the mail safely.
Solve the problems and follow the route with the
correct answer.

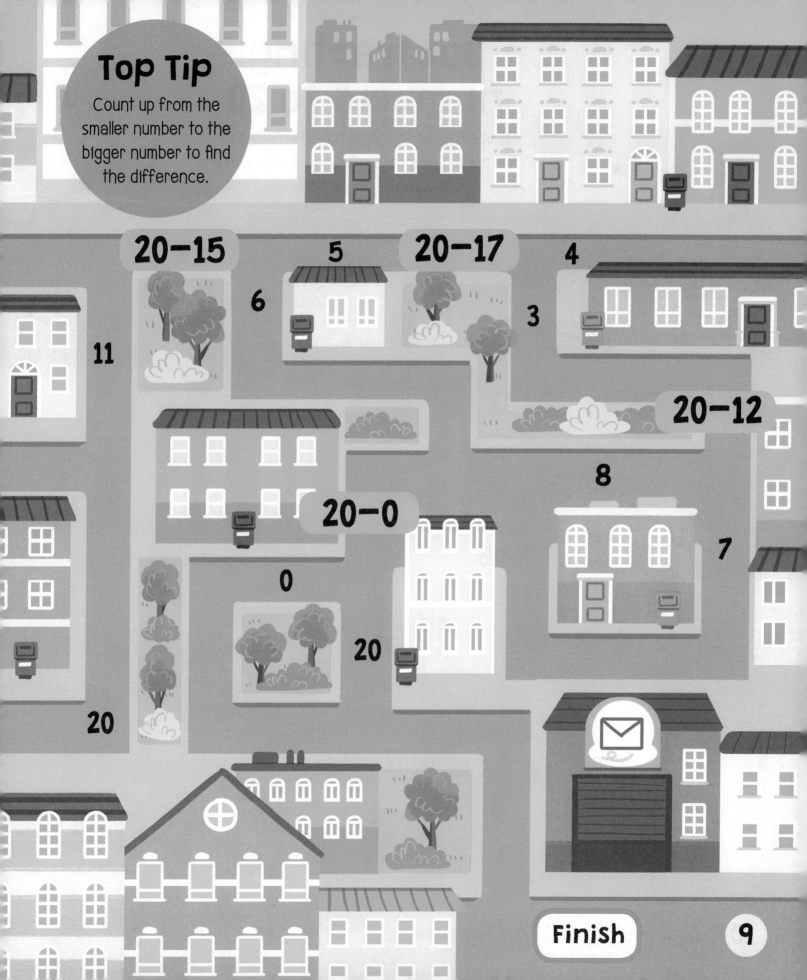

Top Tip

Count up from the smaller number to the bigger number to find the difference.

20–15

5

20–17

4

6

3

11

20–12

20–0

8

0

7

20

20

Finish   9

Subtracting numbers to 20

Guide the ducks through the farmyard to the pond. Solve the problems and follow the path with the correct answer.

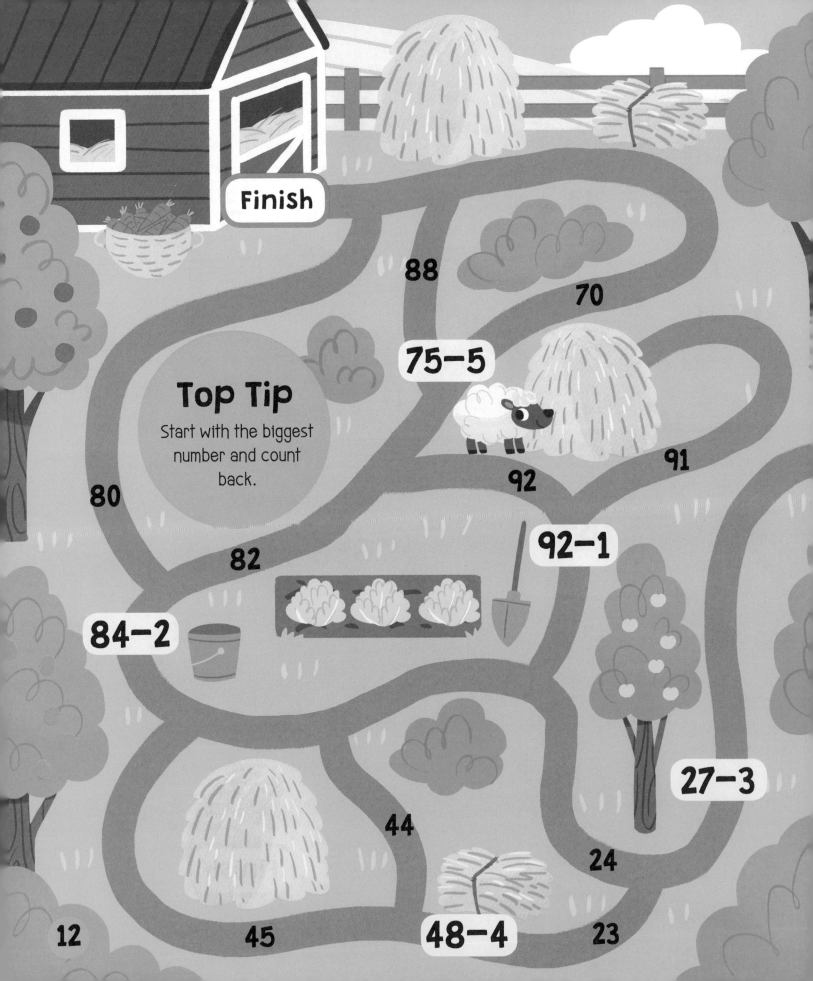

71

76−4

72

63

66

68−5

31

4

34−3

Start

Subtracting within 100

Lead the cow back to the shed. Avoid the hay
bales on the way! Solve the calculations and
follow the correct answers.

13

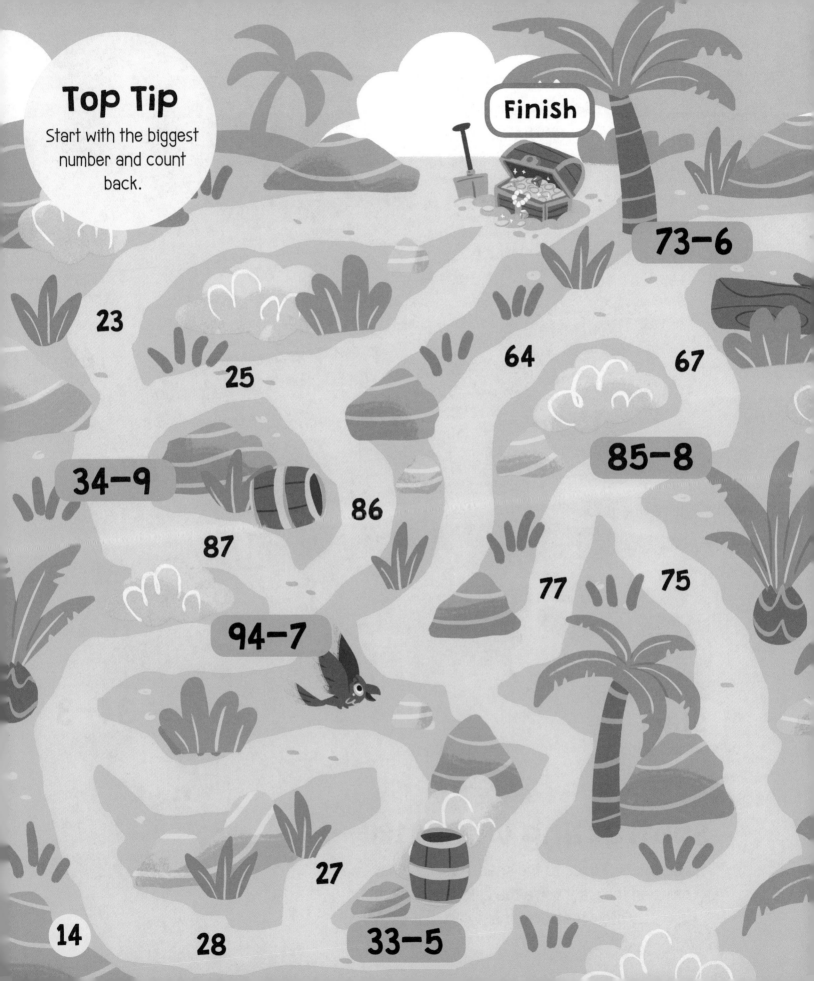

Top Tip
Start with the biggest number and count back.

Finish

73 – 6

23

25

64

67

34 – 9

85 – 8

86

87

77

75

94 – 7

27

14

28

33 – 5

More subtracting within 100

Can you help the pirate to find the treasure? Solve the calculations and follow the correct answers.

Start

72-5

67

66

28-9

19

53-4

17

29

39

35-6

48

49

64-7

57

56

78

77

86-8

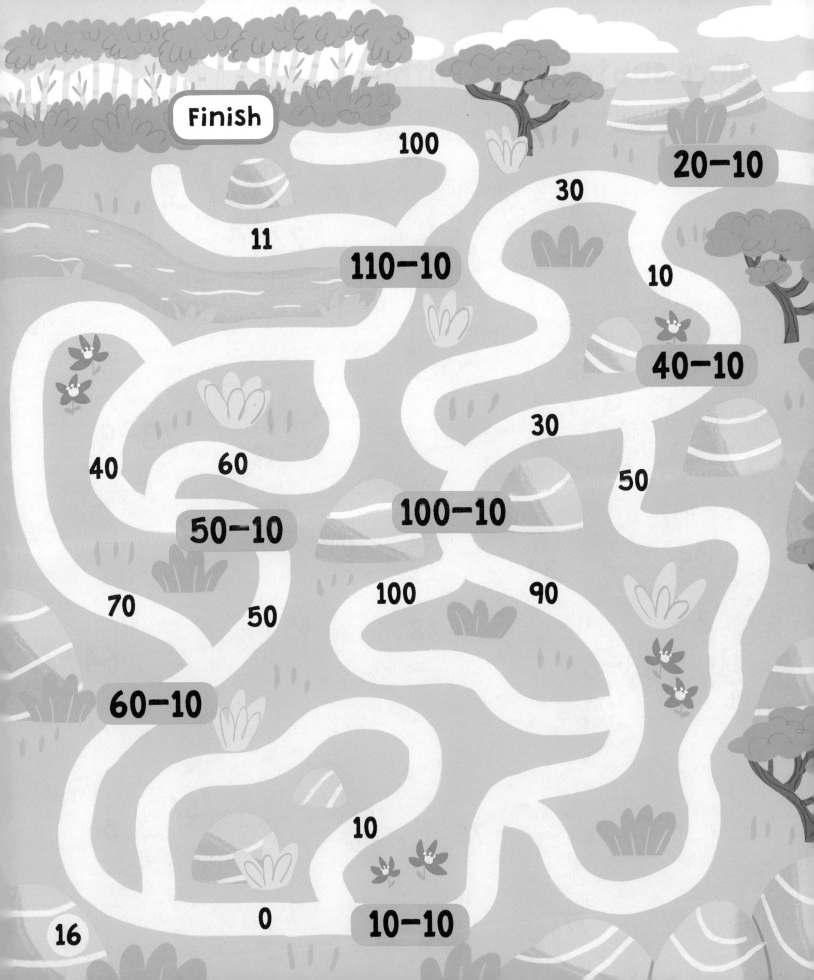

Finish

100

20–10

30

11

110–10

10

40–10

30

40   60   50

100–10

50–10

70   50

100   90

60–10

10

0   10–10

16

70

90

80 − 10

80

70 − 10

Top Tip
Use your number bonds
to 10 to help you.
5 − 1 = 4
50 − 10 = 40

60

80

100

20

90 − 10

30 − 10

40

Subtracting 10
Help the panda make her way to the
bamboo! Solve the calculations and follow
the correct answers.

Start

Subtracting multiples of 10

Help the superhero to confront the alien. Solve the calculations and follow the correct answers.

70−30   50

40

80−70   20

Finish

10

80−30

90−50   30

40   40

90−70   20

10

60−50

50

20

30

Top Tip
Use your number bonds to 10 to help you.
6 − 3 = 3
60 − 30 = 30

19

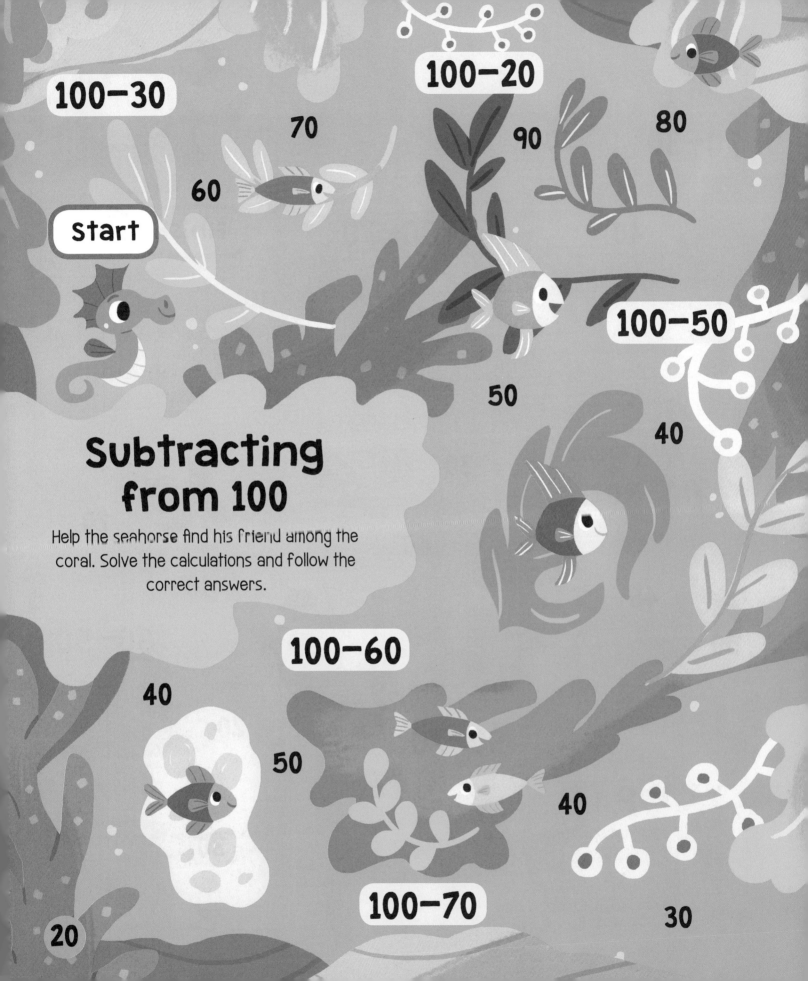

Subtracting from 100

Help the seahorse find his friend among the coral. Solve the calculations and follow the correct answers.

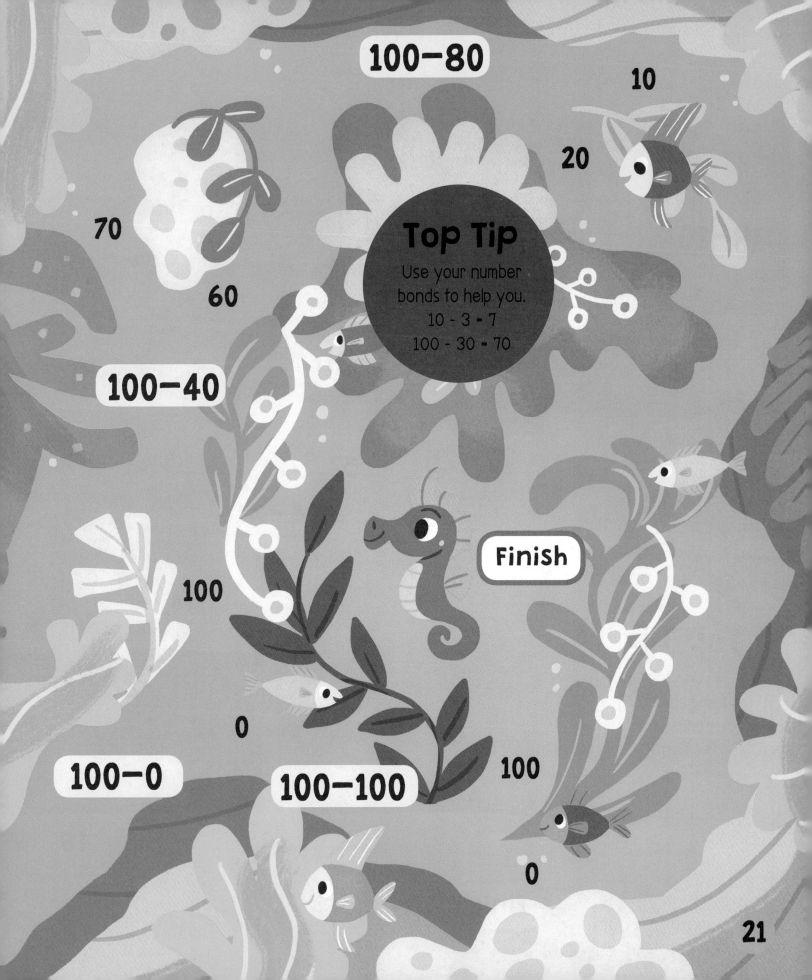

100-80

10

20

70

60

Top Tip
Use your number
bonds to help you.
10 - 3 - 7
100 - 30 - 70

100-40

100

Finish

0

100-0

100-100

100

0

21

89-10

33

23

23

69

79

53-30

27

73-50

77-20

57

84-40

67

34

44

28-40

Top Tip
When you subtract a number ending in 0, the units stay the same.

8

18

Finish

22

43

92−50

42

26

28

36−20

16

18

68−40

44

33

Subtracting 10s from two-digit numbers

Help the prince find his way to the sword in the stone. Solve the problems and follow the path with the correct answers.

83−50

47

start

67−30

37

52

96−45

51

63

62

84−22

24

26

Subtracting
two-digit numbers

Help the baby turtle find his way across the sand and
past the rocks to his mother. Solve the subtraction
problems and follow the path with the correct answers.

38−12

25

56−31

26

Start

24

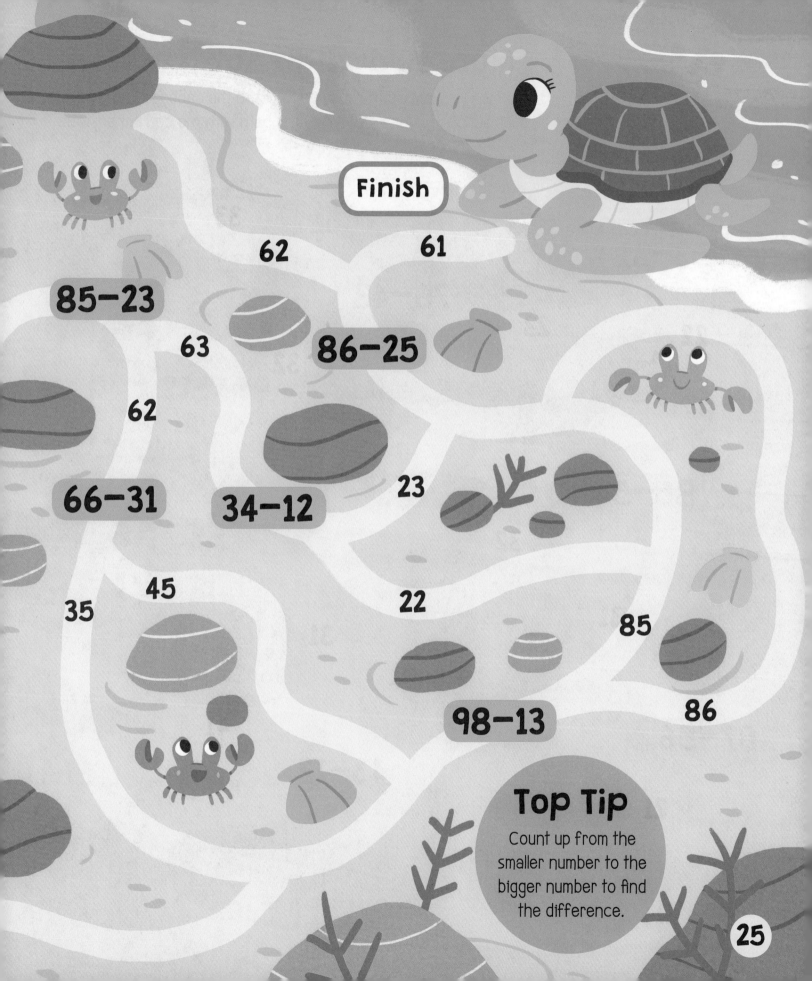

Finish

62   61

85–23

63   86–25

62

66–31   34–12   23

45   22

35   85

98–13   86

Top Tip
Count up from the
smaller number to the
bigger number to find
the difference.

25

More two-digit subtraction

Which way should the snail go to get to the cabbage? Solve the subtraction problems and follow the path with the correct answers.

Start

53–31

76–43

33

22

23

32

85–54

32

31

31

67–56

41

43–12

21

11

26

59-25

34

35

42

97-45

52

Top Tip
Take away the units and then the tens.

56

65

73-22

52

51

69-13

84-41

Finish

43

44

Missing numbers

Help the robot find the computer. Calculate the answer and follow the route with the correct missing number.

Start

$67 - \boxed{} = 64$

3

4

$85 - \boxed{} = 81$

4

5

$\boxed{} - 5 = 42$

46

47

$58 - \boxed{} = 51$

4

7

69

$\boxed{} - 2 = 67$

28

65

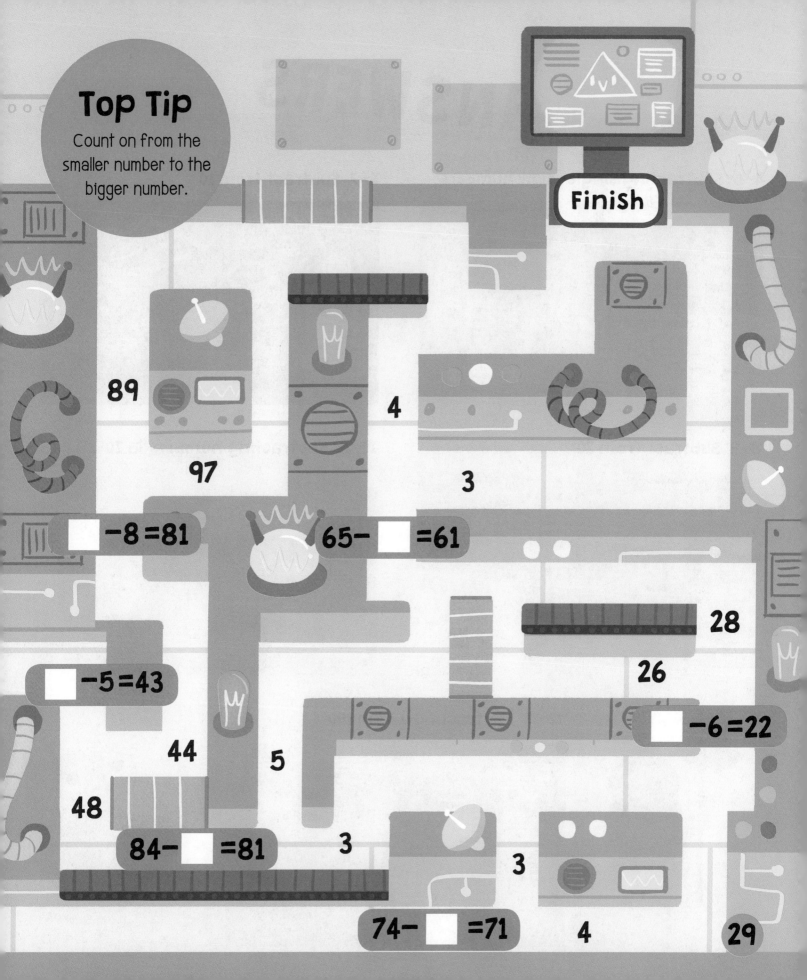

Top Tip
Count on from the smaller number to the bigger number.

Finish

89

4

97

3

☐ −8 =81

65− ☐ =61

☐ −5 =43

28

26

☐ −6 =22

44

5

48

84− ☐ =81

3

3

74− ☐ =71

4

29

ANSWERS

4-5 Subtracting single-digit numbers

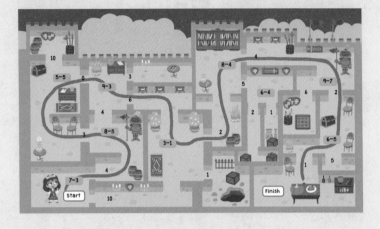

6-7 Subtract from 10

8-9 Subtract from 20

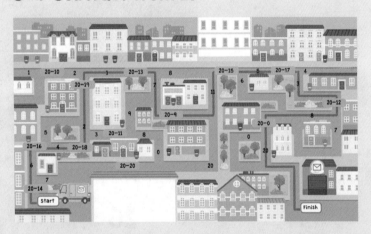

10-11 Subtracting numbers to 20

12-13 Subtracting within 100

14–15 More subtracting within 100

16–17 Subtracting 10

18–19 Subtracting multiples of 10

20–21 Subtracting from 100

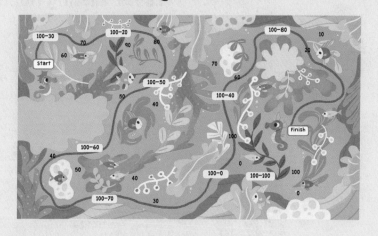

22–23 Subtracting 10s from two-digit numbers

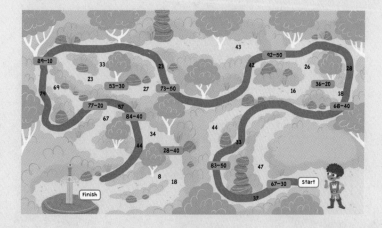

24-25 Subtracting two-digit numbers

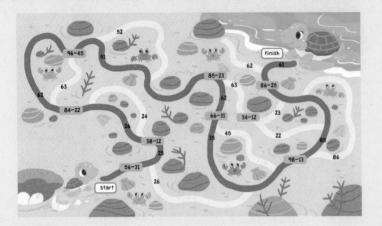

26-27 More two-digit subtraction

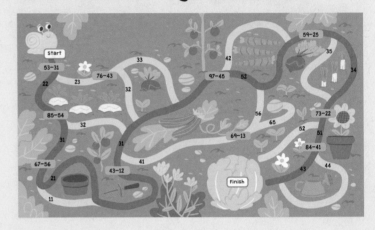

28-29 Missing numbers

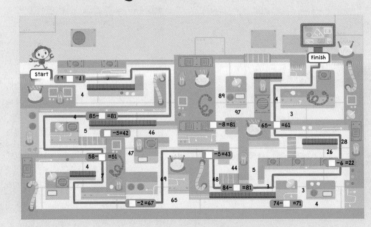